A Peace and Plenty Quilt Book

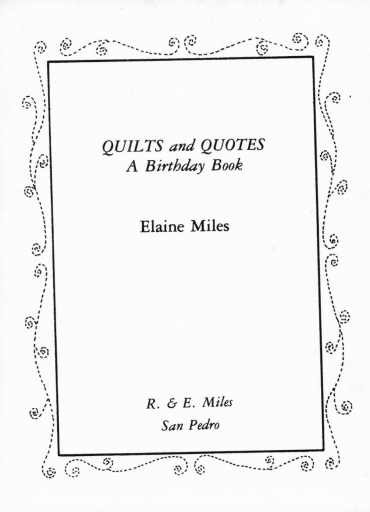

QUILTS and QUOTES
A Birthday Book

Elaine Miles

R. & E. Miles
San Pedro

ACKNOWLEDGEMENTS

The author would like to thank the following authors and publishers for being so generous with their permissions:

January 9: "Yes, we were raised up hard...."
March 18: "Quilts, although born of necessity...."
Reprinted from *Award Winning Quilts*, by Effie Chalmers Pforr, Copyright © 1974 by Oxmoor House, Inc., Birmingham, Alabama, by permission.

January 25: "When nights are cold...."
September 7: "She sews the bits together...."
Reprinted from *Quilter's Newsletter*, the first Copyright © 1970, and the second (originally published in 1930 by the Gertrude May Art Studio) Copyright © 1973, by Leman Publications, Bonnie Leman, Editor, by permission.

January 29: "How can a few notes...."
September 9: "Neighborliness is not love...."
December 10: "Needlework is the art...."
Reprinted from *Woman's Day Book of American Needlework*, by Rose Wilder Lane, Copyright © 1961, 1962, 1963 by Fawcett Publications, Inc., reprinted by permission of Simon and Shuster, Inc.

Mass.: The Belknap Press of Harvard University Press, Copyright © 1951, 1955 by the President and Fellows of Harvard College.

August 24: "But the lasting thought...." Reprinted from *American Antiques* (July 1977), "American Patchwork: A Story Within a Story," by Barb Riley, Copyright © 1977 by Lindencroft Publications, Inc., by permission.

September 13: "...see how often quilts...." Reprinted from *Quiltmakers Time, Book One*, Copyright © 1972 by Sally Goodspeed, by permission.

October 7: "Green leaves, golden leaves...."
November 4: "Life is like a patchwork quilt...."
December 28: "Each fragment there...." Reprinted from *The Romance of the Patchwork Quilt in America*, by Carrie A. Hall and Rose G. Kretsinger, Copyright © 1935 by The Caxton Printers Ltd., Caldwell, Idaho, by permission.

December 31: "The Broken Resolution." Reprinted from *A Net of Fireflies*, translated by Harold Stewart, Copyright © 1960 by Charles E. Tuttle Co., by permission.

And finally, two special acknowledgements:
— to all the people, mostly unknown, who have been responsible for the magnificent legacy of patches; and
— to Eliza Calvert Hall for her beautiful book, *Aunt Jane of Kentucky*.

PREFACE

Birthday books have always seemed to me to fulfill admirably William Morris's injunction that possessions be both useful and beautiful. It is hoped that this little book will prove no exception. To mark each day of the year, there is either a quilt block or a "companion" quotation. Some are very famous, some are not so well known. In the quilt world there are hundreds of designs, and all have names. Most have more than one, and some, like *Indian Trail*, have as many as a dozen. Often one name will apply to more than one patch, as in the case of *Road to California*, or that quilt, beloved of brides, *Rose of Sharon*. Time, place, circumstance, or the quiltmaker's preference would dictate the difference.

Quilts were a large part of every woman's life. They were made because they had to be, but they also served the purposes of beauty, relaxation, artistic expression, and an acceptable excuse for social gatherings. It is no surprise, therefore, that the names of the blocks came from things that were important in the lives of the women who made them. They were inspired by nature, religion, political events, occupations, everyday happenings, hopes, and dreams.

The quotes are an attempt to capture the essence of the time and life from which the quilts sprang. There are lines from the Bible, old songs, poems, sayings, an occasional historical fact, and the thoughts of some contemporary quiltmakers on the subject. A few quotes were chosen just because I liked them and they suggested a certain block to me. All in all it seems a most natural wedding — words and quilt blocks. I hope the result will bring pleasure and maybe a little inspiration to patchwork lovers everywhere.

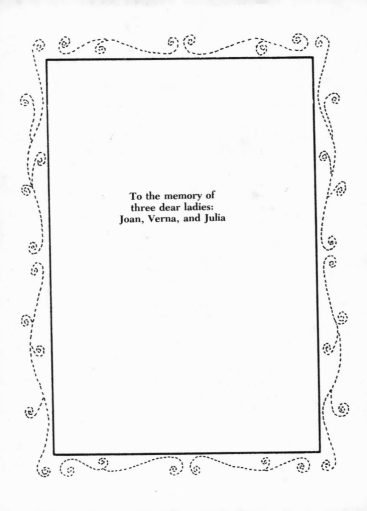

**To the memory of
three dear ladies:
Joan, Verna, and Julia**

JANUARY

Quilts were one of life's necessities, and it was important, therefore, that every little girl learn the craft of making them as soon as she could hold a needle. She started with the simplest patch and learned as she worked. Ideally she had twelve tops pieced by the time she was ready to marry.

Simple
Nine Patch

This needlework of mine may tell
That when a child I learned well
And by my elders I was taught
Not to spend my time for nought....

From an old sampler

JANUARY

Ann Yearly[1] 38

[2]

Chris Barlow[3] 47

JANUARY

*North
Carolina Lily*

Flowers, Plants and Fishes
Beasts, Birds, Flyes and Bees
Hills, Dales, Plains, Pastures
Skies, Seas, Rivers, Trees,
There's nothing near at hand or farthest sought
But with the needle may be wrought.

From an old sampler

Brown Goose

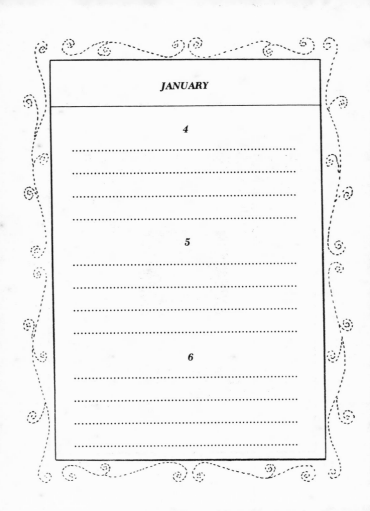

JANUARY

4

....
....
....
....

5

....
....
....
....

6

....
....
....
....

Small skill is gained by those who cling to ease;
The hardy sailor hails from stormy seas.
Old saying

*Storm
at Sea*

Yes, we were raised up hard, but I'm proud of
what I've done. And my quilting has been one of
the proudest things I've done.

Mrs. W.A. Odom

JANUARY

Doug Yearly 37

....

....

....

8

....

....

....

9

....

....

....

Dolly Madison's Star

Who can find a virtuous woman? for her price is far above rubies.
The heart of her husband doth safely trust in her....

Proverbs 31: 10-11.

Martha Washington's Star

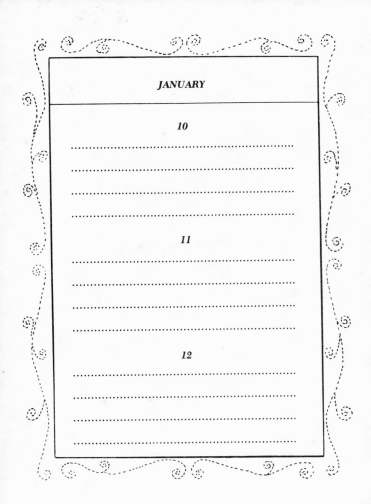

JANUARY

10

....
....
....
....

11

....
....
....
....

12

....
....
....
....

JANUARY

Which is the Wind that brings the cold?
  The North Wind, Freddy, and all the snow
And the sheep will scamper into the fold
  When the North begins to blow.

Edmund Clarence Stedman

*North
Wind*

Winter Memory

Outside—the night was dark and cold,
The North Wind blowing up a storm.
Inside—beneath the quilts of old,
I lay secure, all safe and warm.

JANUARY

13

....
....
....
....
....

Brewster   Per kins 43

14

....
....
....
....

15

....
....
....
....
....

Tree of Temptation

And the devil, taking him up into an high mountain, shewed unto him all the kingdoms of the world in a moment of time. And the devil said unto him, All this power will I give thee, and the glory of them....If thou therefore wilt worship me, all shall be thine. And Jesus answered and said unto him, Get thee behind me, Satan....

Luke 4:5-8.

Devil's Claws

JANUARY

16

....
....
....
....

17

....
....
....
....

18

Natalie Richards................23
....
....
....

To see a world in a grain of sand
And a heaven in a wild flower,
Hold Infinity in the palm of your hand
And Eternity in an hour.

William Blake

*Eternal
Triangle*

To work with quilts is to work with Infinity and
Eternity on a very human scale.

JANUARY

19

....
....
....
....

20

....
....
....
....

21

....
....
....
....

JANUARY

Bear's Paw

Patchwork? Ah, no! It was memory, imagination, history, biography, joy, sorrow, philosophy, religion, romance, realism, life, love, and death; and over all, like a halo, the love of the artist for his work and the soul's longing for earthly immortality.

Eliza Calvert Hall

Grape Basket

JANUARY

22

....
....
....
....

23

....
....
....
....

24

....
....
....
....

JANUARY

When nights are cold and you need an extra
cover, a store bought blanket will stop your
shivers, but a handmade quilt will warm your
soul.

Bonnie Leman

*Blackford's
Beauty*

If of thy mortal goods thou art bereft,
And of thy store two loaves alone are left,
Sell one, and with the dole
Buy hyacinths to feed thy soul.

Sadi

JANUARY

25

....
....
....
....

26

....
....
....
....

27

....
....
....
....

*Missouri
Puzzle*

How can a few notes of music, some paint on canvas, mere pieces of cloth sewed together, have this power to lift the human spirit? No one can explain this; it is the mystery of art.
                                        Rose Wilder Lane

*Dutchman's
Puzzle*

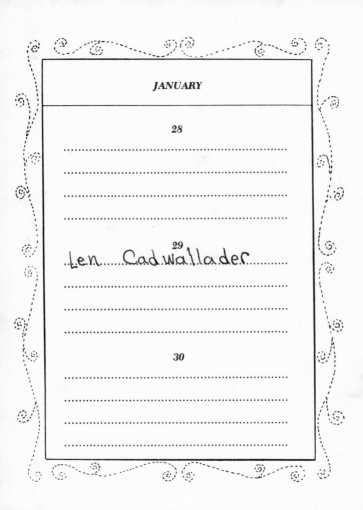

JANUARY

28

....
....
....
....

29

Len Cadwallader..........

....
....
....

30

....
....
....
....

Lost, yesterday, somewhere between sunrise and sunset, two golden hours, each set with sixty diamond minutes. No reward is offered, for they are gone forever.

Horace Mann

Hourglass

Everything has a time. I get all my work done in its proper time....When all my chores are tended, it puts me in mind to get to my quilting.

Quirl Thompson Havenhill

JANUARY-FEBRUARY

31

....
....
....
....

1

....
....
....
....

2

Peter + Debbie A73

....
....
....

FEBRUARY

*Job's
Troubles*

So went Satan forth from the presence of the
Lord, and smote Job with sore boils from the
sole of his foot unto his crown.

Job 2:7.

*Job's
Tears*

FEBRUARY

3

Cheri Wing-Jones 53

....

....

....

4

....

....

....

....

5

....

....

....

....

FEBRUARY

And the stately ships go on
   To their haven under the hill;
But O for the touch of a vanished hand,
   And the sound of a voice that is still!
                              Alfred, Lord Tennyson

*Lost
Ship*

Here's a piece of Miss Penelope's dress, but
where's Miss Penelope? Ain't it strange that a
piece of calico will outlast you and me?
                              Eliza Calvert Hall

FEBRUARY

6

Pam Barlow 43

....

....

....

7

....

....

....

....

8

Ac's 51

....

....

....

....

FEBRUARY

*Grandmother's
Favorite*

My whole life is in that quilt. It scares me sometimes when I look at it. All my joys and all my
sorrows are stitched into those little pieces...I
tremble sometimes when I remember what that
quilt knows about me.
*An Ohio great-grandmother reminiscing
to Marguerite Ickis*

Ohio Star

FEBRUARY

9

....
....
....
....

10

Carlton Barlow 40

....
....
....

11

Helen R 53

....
....
....

FEBRUARY

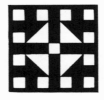

*Lincoln's
Platform*

During the 1858 Illinois campaign for United States Senator there was a series of seven debates involving the two contestants: the famous and sophisticated incumbent, Stephen Douglas (affectionately known as "The Little Giant"), and a relatively unknown challenger and country boy, Abraham Lincoln. Douglas was re-elected, but the debates made Lincoln a national figure, and the Republican presidential nominee in 1860.

*Little
Giant*

FEBRUARY

12

....
....
....
....

13

....
....
....
....

14

....
....
....
....

Fancy or plain...quilts seem...symbolic of some of our finer human qualities.

The Foxfire Book

Hole in the Barn Door

Sleep under a new quilt and your dreams will come true.

Old saying

FEBRUARY

15
Jeffery Toothaker 54

16

17
Grammie Y

FEBRUARY

Mosaic

I thought about the man that laid the pavement in that old church, and wondered what his name was, and how he looked, and what he'd think if he knew there was an old woman down here in Kentucky using his patterns to make a bedquilt.
Eliza Calvert Hall

Tile Puzzle

FEBRUARY

18

....
....
....
....

19

....
....
....
....

20

....
....
....
....

FEBRUARY

Fredericksburg, V. 1778
In the name of God, Amen.
I give to my son, Gen. George Washington, all
my land in Accockeek Run, in the County of Staf-
ford...to him and his heirs forever, also my best
bed, bedstead...and my quilted blue and white
quilt, and my best dressing glass.
Mary Ball Washington

*Washington's
Own*

We can tell how precious quilts were to their
owners by the fact that they, along with other
treasures, were bequeathed to beloved heirs.

FEBRUARY

21

....
....
....
....

22

Sarah Kate Perkins   73

....
....
....
....

23

....
....
....
....

Rolling Stone

As the rolling stone gathers no moss, so the roving heart gathers no affections.

Anna Jameson

Wandering Foot

FEBRUARY

Amy Dunbar [24] 58

M+D Peelle [25] A.44

Reginald Eric Richards [26]

FEBRUARY

Susan B. Anthony is said to have delivered her
first speech on Women's Suffrage in Cleveland,
Ohio, at a church quilting bee.

*Sister's
Choice*

[At that quilting bee] one might have learned...
how to bring up babies by hand; how to mend a
cracked teapot; how to take out grease from a
brocade; how to reconcile absolute decrees with
free will; how to make five yards of cloth answer
the purpose of six; and how to put down the
Democratic party.

Harriet Beecher Stowe

FEBRUARY

27

....
....
....
....

28

....
....
....
....

29

....
....
....
....

MARCH

*Windblown
Square*

I saw you toss the kites on high
And blow the birds about the sky;
And all around I heard you pass,
Like ladies' skirts across the grass —
                    Robert Louis Stevenson

Whirlwind

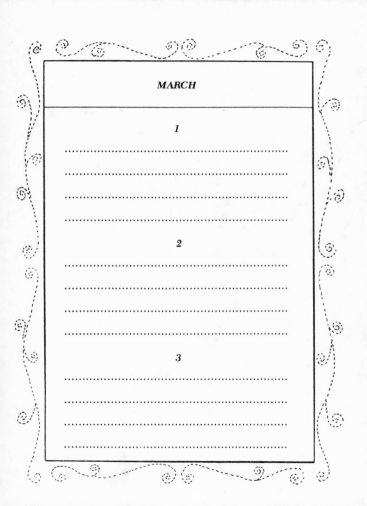

MARCH

1

....
....
....
....

2

....
....
....
....

3

....
....
....
....

*Kansas
Dugout*

Mama's best quilts were her dugout quilts,
because that was when she really needed something pretty.

Odessa Wilman

*Queen
Butterfly*

MARCH

Doug   Yearly Jr.[4]   60
Peter   Richards   54

Agnus   Pelle[5]   50

[6]

~~Names~~
Samuel   Peelle   85

Susannah

I came from Salem City
With my washpan on my knee,
I'm going to California
The gold dust for to see.
Oh Susanna, don't you cry for me!

Traditional, U.S.A.

*Prairie
Queen*

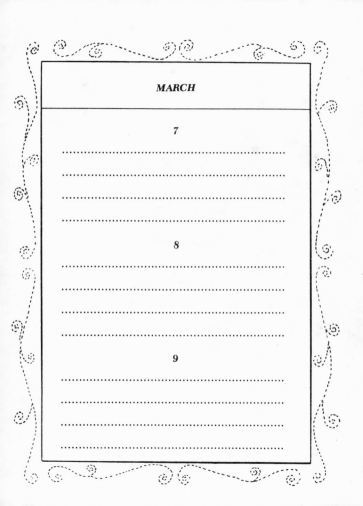

MARCH

7

....
....
....
....

8

....
....
....
....

9

....
....
....
....

One of Mary's quilts she called the Star and Crescent....She got the pattern from a Mrs. Lefferts, one of the new Pennsylvania Dutch families, and pieced it this winter.

From a letter written in Ohio, 1841

Star and Crescent

The quilts done by the Dutch in Long Island and the Germans in Pennsylvania have always been distinguished by their exquisite quilting and intricate seaming on the curve.

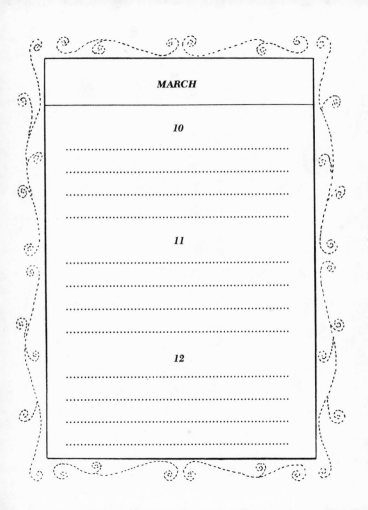

MARCH

10

....
....
....
....

11

....
....
....
....

12

....
....
....
....

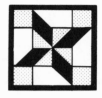

Clay's Choice

Let us now praise famous men, and our fathers that begat us....Their bodies are buried in peace; but their name liveth for evermore.
Ecclesiasticus 44:1, 14

Nelson's Victory

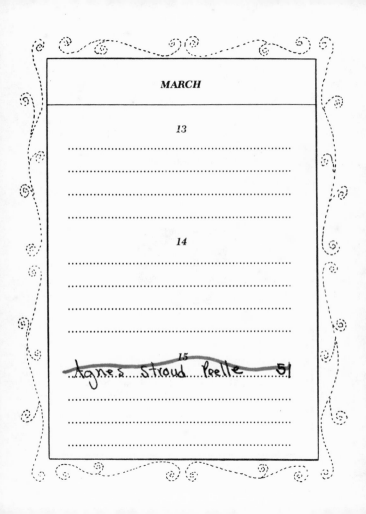

MARCH

13

....
....
....
....

14

....
....
....
....

15

Agnes Stroud Peelle   51

....
....
....

MARCH

It begat habits of peace and patience in those that professed and practiced it.
Sir Henry Wotton

Patience Corner

Quilts, although born of necessity, were the conception of love and the fruition of hours of labor.
Effie Chalmers Pforr

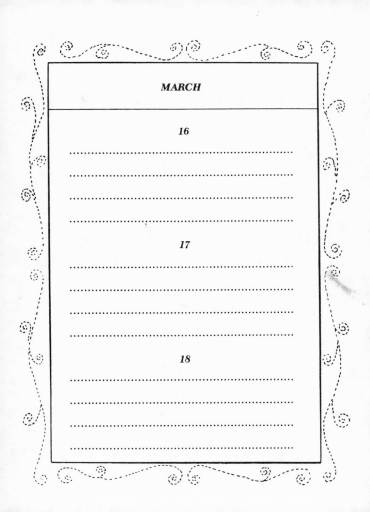

MARCH

16

....
....
....
....

17

....
....
....
....

18

....
....
....
....

*Road to
California*

Does the road wind up-hill all the way?
Yes, to the very end.
Will the day's journey take the whole long day?
From morn to night, my friend.
                    Christina Georgina Rossetti

*Road to
Oklahoma*

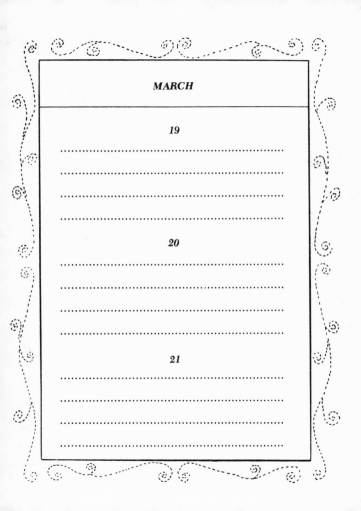

MARCH

19

....
....
....
....

20

....
....
....
....

21

....
....
....
....

MARCH

A quilting bee not only accomplished a necessary task but was one of the few excuses for socializing in an era when distances were great and time too valuable to be spent unproductively. In the evening the frames were put aside and the men arrived for eating, singing, dancing, and, for the younger ones, courting.

Swing in the Center

In the sky the bright stars glittered,
  On the banks the pale moon shone,
And 'twas from Aunt Dinah's quilting party
  I was seeing Nellie home.

Stephen Foster

MARCH

22

....
....
....
....

23

....
....
....
....

24

....
....
....
....

MARCH

Windmill

When the well's dry, we know the worth of water.

Benjamin Franklin

*Water
Wheel*

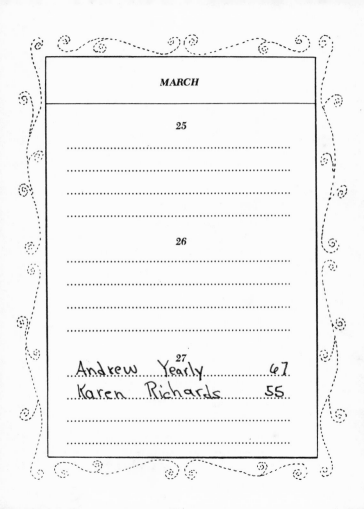

MARCH

25

....
....
....
....

26

....
....
....
....

27

Andrew Yearly   67
Karen Richards   55

....
....

MARCH

Count that day lost whose low descending sun
Views from thy hand no worthy action done.

Old Saying

*Night
and Day*

I've been a hard worker all my life...but 'most all
my work has been the kind that "perishes with
the using...." But when one of my grand-
children...sees one of these quilts they'll think
about Aunt Jane, and, wherever I am then, I'll
know I ain't forgotten.

Eliza Calvert Hall

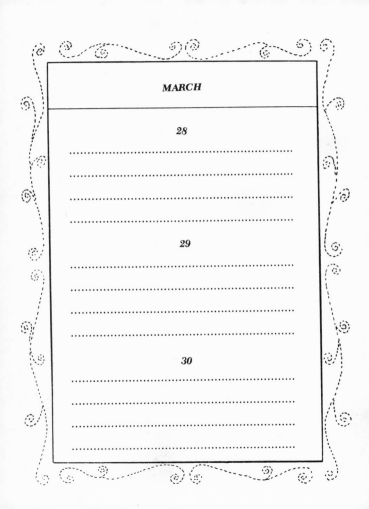

MARCH

28

....
....
....
....

29

....
....
....
....

30

....
....
....
....

**Rising
Sun**

I'll tell you how the Sun rose—
A Ribbon at a time—
The Steeples swam in Amethyst—
The news, like Squirrels, ran—
The Hills untied their Bonnets—
The Bobolinks—begun—
Then I said softly to myself—
"That must have been the Sun"!

Emily Dickinson

Ribbons

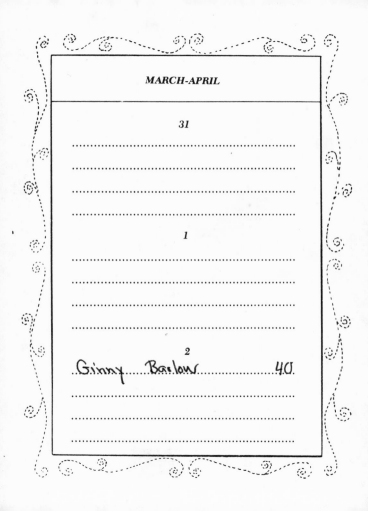

MARCH-APRIL

31

....
....
....
....

1

....
....
....
....

2

Ginny Barlow .... 40.
....
....
....

The frugal snail, with forecast of repose,
Carries his house with him where'er he goes....
Charles Lamb

*Snail's
Trail*

The kind of world one carries about in oneself is
the important thing, and the world outside takes
all its graces, color   and value from that.
James Russell Lowell

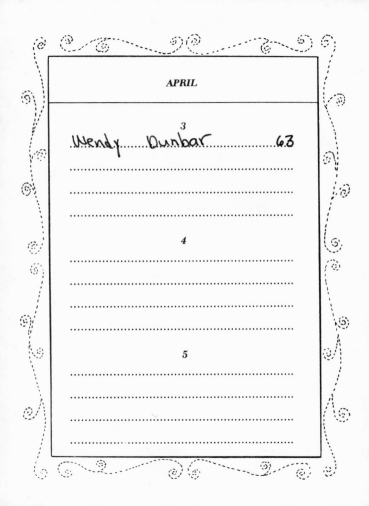

APRIL

3

Wendy Dunbar 63

4

5

APRIL

Hosanna

[They] took branches of palm trees, and went forth to meet him, and cried, Hosanna: Blessed is the King of Israel that cometh in the name of the Lord.

John 12:13.

Crown of Thorns

APRIL

6

....
....
....
....

7

....
....
....
....

8

....
....
....
....

APRIL

In the spring a young man's fancy
lightly turns to thoughts of love.
Alfred, Lord Tennyson

*Young
Man's Fancy*

The quilting was in those days considered the most solemn and important recognition of a betrothal.

Harriet Beecher Stowe

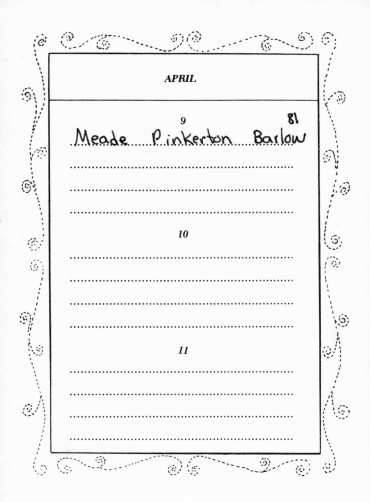

APRIL

Meade   Pinkerton   Barlow

9

10

11

81

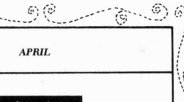

APRIL

*Cross
and Crown*

**Bring forth the royal diadem
And crown Him, crown Him—**
From the old hymn, Coronation

*King's
Crown*

APRIL

12

....
....
....
....

13

....
....
....
....

14

....
....
....
....

Life looks beyond the hands of time
Where what we now deplore
Shall rise in full immortal flower
And bloom to fade no more.
Inscription on a Friendship Quilt, 1849

*Tree
Everlasting*

I reckon everybody wants to leave something
behind that'll last after they're dead and gone. It
don't look like it's worthwhile to live unless you
can do that.

Eliza Calvert Hall

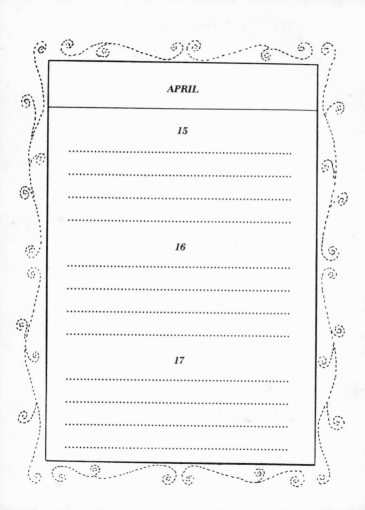

APRIL

15

....
....
....
....

16

....
....
....
....

17

....
....
....
....

APRIL

*Rare
Old Tulip*

We owe the popularity of the tulip in our American quilts to the early Dutch settlers. The tulip originally came from Persia where it was a symbol for love, and when first imported into Holland, a bulb was said to be worth the price of a "coach and four."

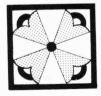

*Grandma's
Pieced Tulip*

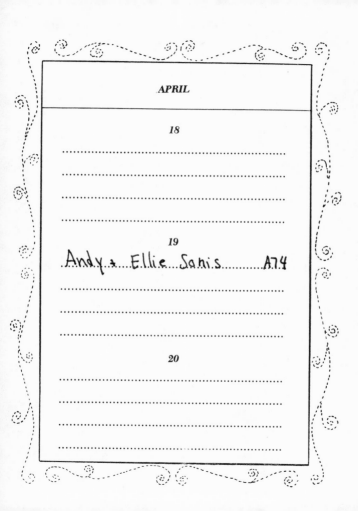

APRIL

18

....
....
....
....

19

Andy & Ellie Sanis A74

....
....
....
....

20

....
....
....
....

APRIL

Toad in a puddle
    Happy as can be—
World's in a muddle,
    But what care he?

*Toad in
a Puddle*

One of the things quilting has taught me is that the world goes on, no matter what, and if we are to survive with any amount of grace we all need little oases of tranquility and sanity in our lives.

APRIL

21

....
....
....
....

22

Nana`...
....
....
....

23

....
....
....
....

*Crowned
Cross*

The way to bliss lies not on beds of down,
And he that has no cross deserves no crown.
Francis Quarles

*Crown
and Cross*

APRIL

24

....
....
....
....

25

....
....
....
....

26

....
....
....
....

APRIL

And the Lord God planted a garden eastward in Eden; and there he put the man whom he had formed.

Genesis 2:8.

*Garden
of Eden*

Life is said to have begun in a garden; and if here was our lost paradise, may not the paradise we hope to gain through death be....another garden in a new earth?

Eliza Calvert Hall

APRIL

27

Kathryn "our daughter" '83'

28

29

*Jack in
the Box*

Working with your hands gives you a chance not
only to create or restore an object, but also to
restore and recreate yourself....

Beth Gutcheon

*Sugar
Loaf*

30

....
....
....
....

Nathan Rejinold Torthaker `85

....
....
....

2

....
....
....
....

MAY

The sun descending in the west
The evening star does shine,
The birds are silent in their nest
And I must seek for mine....

William Blake

Bird's Nest

He sings to the wide world, and she to her nest—
In the nice ear of Nature which song is best?
James Russell Lowell

MAY

3

....
....
....
....

4

....
....
....
....

5

....
....
....
....

MAY

Peony

For, lo, the winter is past, the rain is over and
    gone;
The flowers appear on the earth; the time of the
    singing of birds is come, and the voice of the
    turtle is heard in our land....

Song of Solomon 2:11-12

*Birds in
the Air*

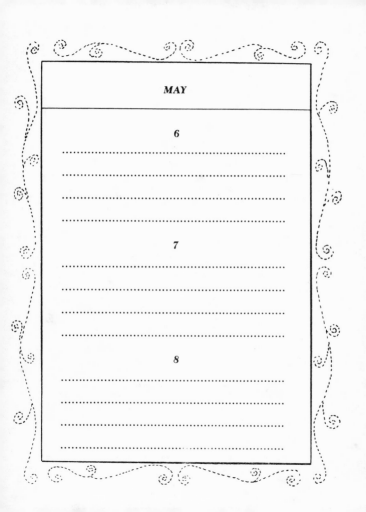

MAY

6

....
....
....
....

7

....
....
....
....

8

....
....
....
....

MAY

Like an army defeated
The snow hath retreated....
Small clouds are sailing,
Blue sky prevailing;
The rain is over and gone!

William Wordsworth

*Flying
Clouds*

The women in the isolation of winter on the prairies pieced their blocks and dreamed of spring, when the wagons could travel once more. The quilts would go into the frames, there would be a quilting bee, and a chance to see other women.

MAY

9

....
....
....
....

10

....
....
....
....

11

David B. Treat   74

....
....
....

MAY

Blue Fields

The little cares that fretted me,
  I lost them yesterday,
Among the fields above the sea,
  Among the winds at play....
Among the hushing of the corn
  Where drowsy poppies nod,
Where ill thoughts die and good are born—
  Out in the fields with God.

Anonymous

Peaceful Hours

MAY

12

....
....
....
....

13

....
....
....
....

14

....
....
....
....

MAY

Under a spreading chestnut tree
  The village smithy stands;
The smith, a mighty man is he,
  With large and sinewy hands;
And the muscles of his brawny arms
  Are strong as iron bands!
        Henry Wadsworth Longfellow

Anvil

Thanks, thanks to thee, my worthy friend,
  For the lesson thou hast taught!
Thus at the flaming forge of life
  Our fortunes must be wrought;
Thus on its sounding anvil shaped
  Each burning deed and thought!
        Henry Wadsworth Longfellow

MAY

15

....
....
....
....

16

....
....
....
....

17

....
....
....
....

MAY

The devil is said to be jealous of anything that is perfect, so as a protection to the person sleeping under a quilt, a subtle imperfection is purposely sewn into it—to catch the devil's eye and distract him from any evil intent he might have.

Crazy Ann

On Flawed Quilts
If a mortal did attain perfection it would be
(To use my grandma's words) the devil's
    mockery.
For God alone forms faultless things,
It shan't be done by human hands.
            Peggy Morgan Cavanaugh

MAY

Sarah Lena[18] Richards 79

Sarah Lena[19] Richards 79 ~~80~~

Karen т Jeff[20]   A 78

MAY

They went till they came to the Delectable
Mountains...to behold the gardens and orchards
the vineyards and fountains of water....

John Bunyan

*Delectable
Mountains*

Through the night of doubt and sorrow
  Onward goes the pilgrim band,
Singing songs of expectation,
  Marching to the promised land.

B.S. Ingemann

MAY

Barlow Peelle [21] 56

Jen Wing Jones [22] 83

[23]

MAY

*English
Flower Garden*

Come into the garden, Maud,
  For the black bat, night, has flown,
Come into the garden, Maud,
  I am here at the gate alone.
                    Alfred, Lord Tennyson

*Flying
Bats*

MAY

24

....
....
....
....

25

....
....
....
....

26

....
....
....
....

MAY

Nae man can tether time or tide.

Robert Burns

*Time
and Tide*

What was any art but an effort to make a sheath,
a mould in which to imprison for a moment the
shining, elusive element which is life itself—life
hurrying past us and running away, too strong to
stop, too sweet to lose?

Willa Cather

MAY

27

....
....
....
....

28

....
....
....
....

29

....
....
....
....

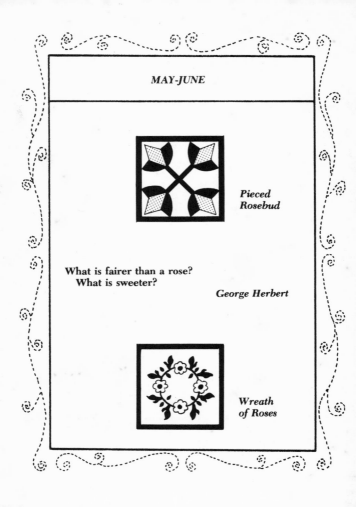

MAY-JUNE

Pieced Rosebud

What is fairer than a rose?
What is sweeter?

George Herbert

Wreath of Roses

MAY-JUNE

30

....
....
....
....

31

....
....
....
....

1

....
....
....
....

JUNE

Doubtless God could have made a better berry,
but doubtless God never did.
William Butler, in praise of strawberries

Strawberry

Have nothing in your houses that you do not
know to be useful, or believe to be beautiful.
William Morris

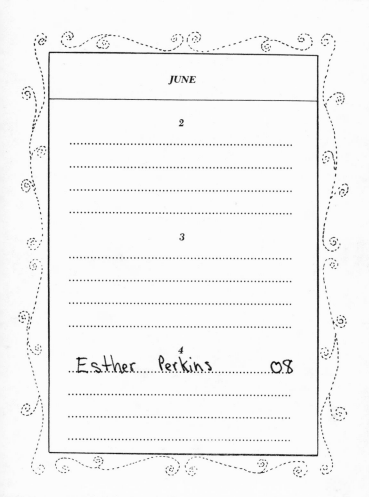

JUNE

2

....
....
....
....

3

....
....
....
....

4
Esther Perkins........... 08
....
....
....

JUNE

*Dusty
Miller*

The mills of the gods grind slowly, but they grind
exceedingly fine.

Old proverb

*Mill
Wheel*

JUNE

5

....
....
....
....

6

....
....
....
....

7

....
....
....
....

JUNE

Sweet Auburn! Loveliest village of the plain,
Where health and plenty cheered the labouring
swain....
How often have I loitered o'er the green,
Where humble happiness endeared each scene!
Oliver Goldsmith

*Our Village
Green*

I love you as I never loved before
Since first I met you on the village green.
James Thornton

JUNE

8

....
....
....
....

82

9

Evan Joseph Murray Waters

....
....
....

10

....
....
....
....

JUNE

I am the rose of Sharon, and the lily of the
   valleys.
As the lily among thorns, so is my love among the
   daughters.

Song of Solomon 2: 1-2.

*Rose of
Sharon*

The applique quilt was a much more extravagant
endeavor than a pieced quilt. Rather than saving
up scraps of material from other projects, whole
cloth was purchased for the specific purpose of
making a quilt. It has come, therefore, to be
regarded as the quilt of prosperity and
occasions. A girl's bridal quilt was usually
appliqued, and *Rose of Sharon* was a favorite
design.

JUNE

DaD Peelle [11]   21

[12]

Judith Perkins [13]   44

JUNE

A beautiful castle I've built for thee,
In dreamland far away,
And there, gentle darling, come dwell with me,
Where love alone has sway.

George Birdseye

*Castle in
the Air*

'Mid pleasures and palaces though we may
   roam,
Be it ever so humble, there's no place like home.
Henry R. Bishop

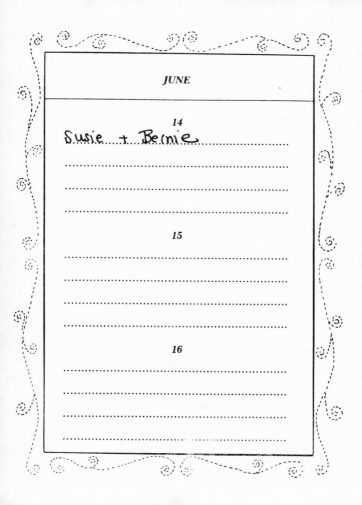

JUNE

14

Susie + Bernie

15

16

JUNE

*Steps to
the Altar*

At your quilting, maids, don't dally,
Quilt quickly if you would marry,
For she who is quiltless at twenty-one
Shall never see her bridal sun.

Old English rhyme

*Old Maid's
Puzzle*

JUNE

17

....
....
....
....

18

....
....
....
....

19

....
....
....
....

JUNE

See first that the design is wise and just; that
ascertained, pursue it resolutely.
William Shakespeare

*Square and
Compass*

I plan my quilts just like I used to plan a house.
Folks say, "How come you quilt so good?" I say,
"If you make careful plans, it will come out
right."

Quirl Thompson Havenhill

JUNE

20

....
....
....
....

21

....
....
....
....

22

....
....
....
....

JUNE

*Mexican
Rose*

O my Luve's like a red, red rose,
   That's newly sprung in June;
O my Luve's like the melodie
   That's sweetly play'd in tune.

Robert Burns

*Wild
Rose*

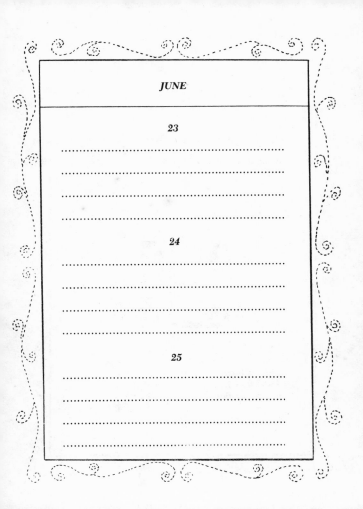

JUNE

23

....
....
....
....

24

....
....
....
....

25

....
....
....
....

JUNE

How falls it, oriole, thou hast come to fly
In tropic splendor through our Northern sky?
At some glad moment was it nature's choice
To dower a scrap of sunset with a voice?

Edgar Fawcett

*Oriole
Window*

A thing of beauty is a joy forever:
Its loveliness increases; it will never
Pass into nothingness....

John Keats

JUNE

George + Barb Austin 75 [26]

Wm K Dunbar IV 59 [27]

[28]

JUNE-JULY

*Love in
a Mist*

Once in the dear dead days beyond recall,
When on the world the mists began to fall,
Out of the dreams that rose in happy throng,
Low to our hearts love sang an old sweet song.
                    Clifton Bingham

*Rose
Dream*

JUNE-JULY

29

....
....
....
....

30

....
....
....
....

1

....
....
....
....

JULY

Skyrocket

**And the rocket's red glare, the bombs bursting in
air,
Gave proof through the night that our flag was
still there.**

Francis Scott Key

*Liberty
Star*

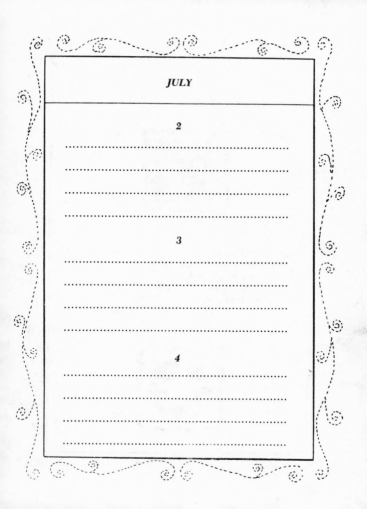

JULY

2

....
....
....
....

3

....
....
....
....

4

....
....
....
....

JULY

*Union
Square*

Sail on, O Ship of State!
Sail on, O Union, strong and great!
Humanity with all its fears,
With all the hopes of future years,
Is hanging breathless on thy fate!
                    Henry Wadsworth Longfellow

*Union
Star*

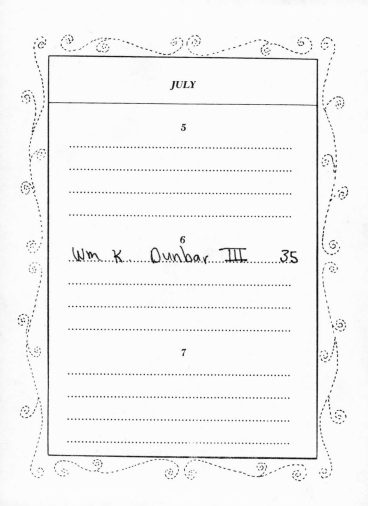

JULY

5

....
....
....
....

6

Wm K Dunbar III 35

....
....
....

7

....
....
....
....

JULY

How doth the little busy bee
  Improve each shining hour,
And gather honey all the day
  From every opening flower!

Isaac Watts

*Honey
Bee*

The women sit around the quilt laughing and as if it isn't a job at all. They never seem to get tired or want to go home. They all seem so content.

Emma Jean Buchanan

JULY

Mom Peelle [8] 22

Alex B. Perkins [9] 71

Bert & Ellen Stevens [10] 76

JULY

Rising Sun

Shine! shine! shine!
Pour down your warmth, great sun!
Walt Whitman

Sunshine

JULY

11

Cathie + Mike .... A. 81

....
....
....

12

....
....
....
....

13

Elizabeth Dunbar 09
Phyllis Wicks ....

....
....

JULY

*Lady of
the Lake*

And locks flung back, and lips apart,
Like monument of Grecian art,
In listening mood she seemed to stand,
The guardian Naiad of the strand.

Sir Walter Scott

*Grecian
Design*

JULY

14

....
....
....
....

15

....
....
....
....

16

....
....
....
....

JULY

*Streak of
Lightning*

Be still, sad heart! and cease repining;
Behind the clouds is the sun still shining;
Thy fate is the common fate of all,
Into each life some rain must fall....
    Henry Wadsworth Longfellow

Sunbeam

JULY

Debbie Richards ......17...... 53

Trina Wicks 18

19

JULY

Ah yet, ere I descend to the grave
May I a small house and large garden have;
And a few friends, and many books, both true,
Both wise, and both delightful too!

Abraham Cowley

*House on
the Hill*

There is something about a quilt that says
people, friendship, community, family, home,
and love.

The Foxfire Book

JULY

20

Austin Perkins 74

21

....

....

....

....

22

D.D. Barlow Jr 12

....

....

....

JULY

The Spider holds a Silver Ball
In unperceived Hands—
And dancing softly to Himself
His Yarn of Pearl—unwinds—....
Emily Dickinson

*Spider
Web*

The web of our life is of a mingled yarn, good
and ill together.

William Shakespeare

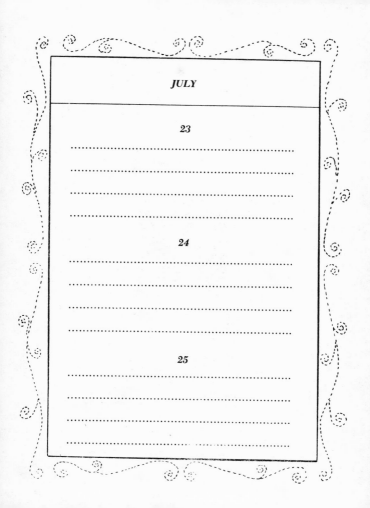

JULY

23

....
....
....
....

24

....
....
....
....

25

....
....
....
....

JULY

Every man is the architect of his own fortune.
Appius Claudius Caecus

Wheel of Fortune

It matters not how strait the gate,
How charged with punishments the scroll,
I am the master of my fate;
I am the captain of my soul.
William Ernest Henley

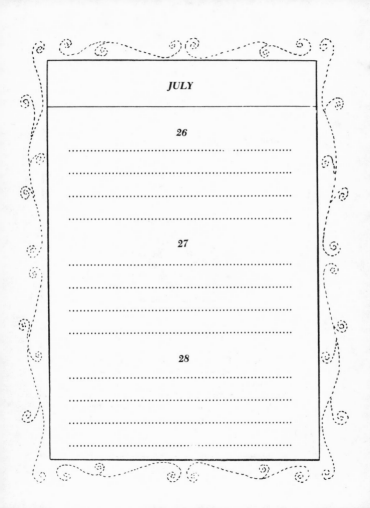

JULY

26

....

....

....

....

....

27

....

....

....

....

....

28

....

....

....

....

....

JULY

I pray, that risen from the dead
   I may in glory stand.
I need no crown upon my head
   But a needle in my hand.

Eugene Field

*Starry
Crown*

To all dispersed sorts of Arts and Trades
I write the needles prayse (that never fades)
So long as children shall be begot and borne,
So long as Hemp or Flax shall be made and
     worne....
Yes, till the world be quite dissolved and past,
So long, at least, the Needles use shall last.

John Taylor

JULY

29

30

D.D.B IV   76

31

Eric Jorgenson   67

Sailboat

**May thy path through life be in the sunshine of
fortune
May soft breezes waft thy gilded bark o'er a
smooth sea to a guileless peaceful shore.**
From a Friendship Quilt, 1849

Sailboat

AUGUST

1

Elizabeth Perkins   44

~~Meann wealy~~   ~~MB~~

2

3

AUGUST

I made every stitch of that spread the year before me and Abram was married....I put it on my bed when we went to housekeeping; it was on the bed when Abram died, and when I die I want them to cover me with it.

Eliza Calvert Hall

Bridal Wreath

In bed we laugh, in bed we cry;
And born in bed, in bed we die.
The near approach a bed may show
Of human bliss to human woe.

Isaac de Benserade

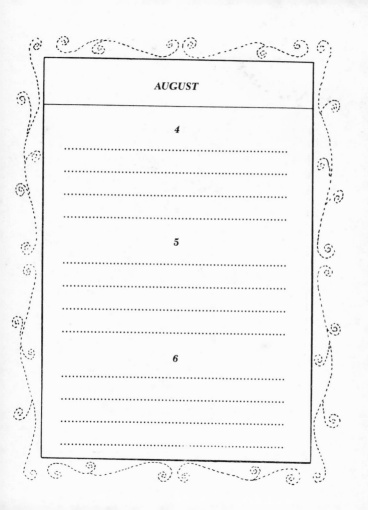

AUGUST

4

....
....
....
....

5

....
....
....
....

6

....
....
....
....

AUGUST

*Path
through
the Woods*

You will find something more in woods than in books. Trees and stones will teach you that which you can never learn from masters.

Saint Bernard

*Forest
Paths*

AUGUST

7

Mary B + Witty 71

....
....
....

8

WRP J. 47

....
....
....
....

9

....
....
....
....

AUGUST

I've travelled about a bit in my time,
And of troubles I've seen a few;
But found it better in every clime
To paddle my own canoe.

Harry Clifton

*Crossed
Canoes*

The greatest thing in the world is to know how to
be sufficient unto oneself.

Michel de Montaigne

AUGUST

10

....
....
....
....

11

Richard Shepherd 41

....
....
....

12

....
....
....
....

AUGUST

*Rocky
Mountain
Puzzle*

What have those lonely mountains worth
revealing?
More glory and more grief than I can tell....
Emily Bronte

*Moon over
the Mountain*

AUGUST

13

....
....
....
....

14

Hannah Linda 85

....
....
....

15

....
....
....
....

AUGUST

*Barrister's
Block*

A lawyer without history or literature is a
mechanic, a mere working mason; if he possesses
some knowledge of these, he may venture to call
himself an architect.

Sir Walter Scott

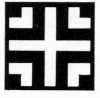

*Stonemason's
Puzzle*

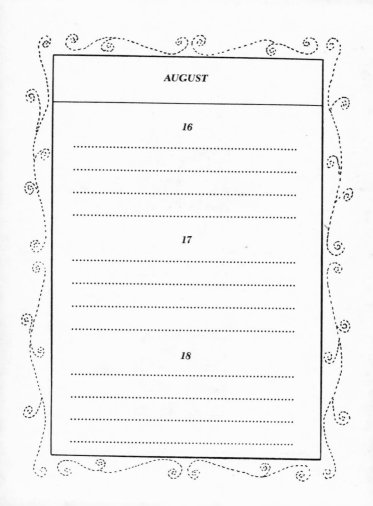

AUGUST

16

....
....
....
....

17

....
....
....
....

18

....
....
....
....

AUGUST

*Milky
Way*

The lights from the parlor and kitchen shone out
    Through the blinds and the windows and bars;
And high overhead and all moving about,
    There were thousands of millions of stars.
                    Robert Louis Stevenson

Blazing Star

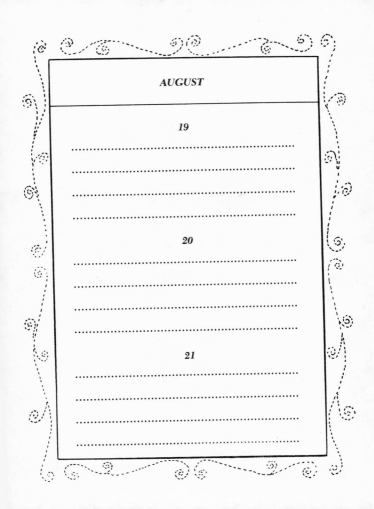

AUGUST

19

....
....
....
....

20

....
....
....
....

21

....
....
....
....

AUGUST

The history of every country begins in the heart
of a man or a woman.

Willa Cather

*Queen
Charlotte's
Crown*

But the lasting thought carried away from any
inspection of a quilted piece is a thought for the
maker. That person whose small regular stitches
transformed bits and pieces into a finished work.
That person who pulled from a hectic passage of
time, an ordered memory. That person is never
far from the quilt.

Barb Riley

AUGUST

Mary Lee Barlow [22] 12
Heather Richards 75

....
....

23

....
....
....
....

24

....
....
....
....

*Pine
Tree*

The Pine Tree is surely the most American of trees. It is found from coast to coast, was for many years the symbol of Colonial America, and in one form or another is the state tree for nine states.

*Tall
Pine Tree*

AUGUST

25
Steve + Elizabeth 72

26

27

AUGUST

For Satan finds some mischief still
  For idle hands to do.

Isaac Watts

*Devil's
Puzzle*

But there never was any time wasted on my
quilts....I did my work faithful; and then, when I
might have set and held my hands, I'd make a
block or two of patchwork, and before long I'd
have enough to put together in a quilt.

Eliza Calvert Hall

AUGUST

28

....
....
....
....

29

Tim + Ansley   A81

....
....
....

30

Jane   Perkins   43

....
....
....

AUGUST-SEPTEMBER

*Indian
Summer*

The golden-rod is yellow,
    The corn is turning brown;
The trees in apple orchards
    With fruit are bending down....
By all these lovely tokens
    September days are here
With summer's best of wealth
    And autumn's best of cheer.

Helen Hunt Jackson

*Little Red
Schoolhouse*

AUGUST-SEPTEMBER

Tara Wicks [31] 62

....

....

....

Poly + Frank [1] 73

....

....

....

[2]

....

....

....

....

SEPTEMBER

For the earth bringeth forth fruit of herself; first the blade, then the ear, after that the full corn in the ear.

Mark 4:28.

Corn and Beans

Oats, peas, beans, and barley grows,
Oats, peas, beans, and barley grows,
Nor you nor I nor anyone knows
How oats, peas, beans, and barley grows.

Children's game

SEPTEMBER

3

....
....
....
....

4

....
....
....
....

5

....
....
....
....

*Flower
Basket*

She sews the bits together,
And, intricate or plain,
Beneath her flying fingers
Grows basket, star or chain.

Grace Noll Crowell

*Odd
Fellow's
Chain*

SEPTEMBER

6

....
....
....
....

7

....
....
....
....

8

....
....
....
....

SEPTEMBER

Neighborliness is not love, not friendship; it may be less than liking. It is the mutual helpfulness of human beings to each other, an unforced, voluntary cooperation springing from a sense of equality in common humanity and human needs.

Rose Wilder Lane

*Next Door
Neighbor*

But we've...lost the concept that a good way to express caring was to do a job of work together... building a barn, getting in the harvest, or quilting a quilt....

Beth Gutcheon

SEPTEMBER

9

....
....
....
....
....

10

E.l.liot Hale Barlow 79

....
....
....
....

11

....
....
....
....

SEPTEMBER

Coxey's Camp

...see how often quilts were more than charming covers. They made statements, celebrated, protected sometimes from more than just cold. They recorded, remembered, signified.

Sally Goodspeed

Kansas Troubles

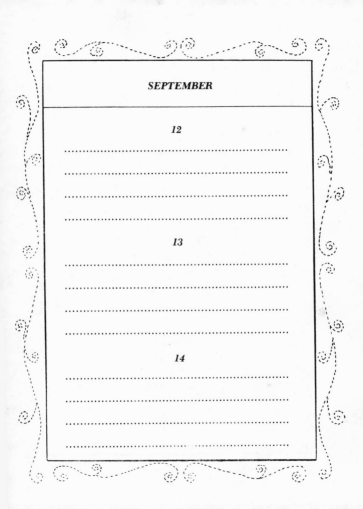

SEPTEMBER

12

....
....
....
....

13

....
....
....
....

14

....
....
....
....

SEPTEMBER

Quick as it fell, from the broken staff
Dame Barbara snatched the silken scarf....
"Shoot, if you must, this old gray head,
But spare your country's flag," she said.
John Greenleaf Whittier

Barbara
Frietchie Star

Those who won our independence....believed
liberty to be the secret of happiness and courage
to be the secret of liberty.
Louis D. Brandeis

SEPTEMBER

15

....
....
....
....

16

....
....
....
....

17

....
....
....
....

*Laurel
Wreath*

So green grows the laurel, and so does the rue,
So woeful, my love, at the parting with you.
                                    Traditional, U.S.A.

*True
Lover's
Knot*

SEPTEMBER

18

....
....
....
....

19

....
....
....
....

20

....
....
....
....

SEPTEMBER

Real joy comes not from ease or riches or from the praise of men, but from doing something worthwhile.

Wilfred Grenfell

Ladies' Delight

I've had a heap of comfort all my life making quilts, and now in my old age I wouldn't take a fortune for them.

Eliza Calvert Hall

SEPTEMBER

21

....
....
....
....

22

....
....
....
....

Anne   Shephard   **23**   06
....
....
....

SEPTEMBER

Glory be to the Father, and to the Son, and to the Holy Ghost; As it was in the beginning, is now, and ever shall be, world without end. Amen.

From The Book of Common Prayer

*World
Without
End*

There are only two or three human stories, and they go on repeating themselves as fiercely as if they had never happened before.

Willa Cather

SEPTEMBER

James Rich Treat 24 76

25

26

SEPTEMBER

**Large streams from little fountains flow,
Tall oaks from little acorns grow.**

David Everett

Oak Leaf

**The most magnificent patchwork quilt has its
beginning in one small piece of material.**

SEPTEMBER

27

Seymour Perkins Jr.   08
Mary B Barlow

28

29

Sandra Yearly   58

*David
and Goliath*

**So David prevailed over the Philistine with a
sling and with a stone, and smote the Philistine,
and slew him....**

1 Samuel 17:50.

*Children
of Israel*

SEPTEMBER-OCTOBER

30

Anna Elizabeth Toothaker

82

....

....

....

1

....

....

....

....

2

....

....

....

....

OCTOBER

'Twixt the optimist and pessimist
  The difference is droll:
The optimist sees the doughnut
  But the pessimist sees the hole.
                    McLandburgh Wilson

*Optical
Illusion*

You can spoil the prettiest quilt pieces that ever
was made just by putting them together with the
wrong color, and the best sort of life is miserable
if you don't look at things right and think about
them right.

                    Eliza Calvert Hall

OCTOBER

Agnes + Billy [3] 81

DeWitt D. Barlow [4] 18.50

Mary + Pete [5] .... A 75

OCTOBER

*Maple
Leaf*

Green leaves, golden leaves,
Tawny, brown, auburn and scarlet—
To spread across the countryside and keep it
warm.
Never was so fine a patchwork quilt
As Autumn stitched that day.

D.A. Lovell

Autumn Tints

OCTOBER

Peter Nielsen [6] 53

Elizabeth M. Barlow [7] 883

[8]

OCTOBER

God moves in a mysterious way,
  His wonders to perform;
He plants his footsteps in the sea,
  And rides upon the storm.

William Cowper

*Wonder of
the World*

Why, who makes much of a miracle?
As to me I know of nothing else but miracles....
To me every hour of the light and dark is a
  miracle,
Every cubic inch of space is a miracle....

Walt Whitman

OCTOBER

9

....
....
....
....

10

....
....
....
....

11

Ansley Newton   52
H+ A's   A 80
....
....

OCTOBER

*Caesar's
Crown*

Render therefore unto Caesar the things which are Caesar's; and unto God the things that are God's.

Matthew 22:21

*Roman
Cross*

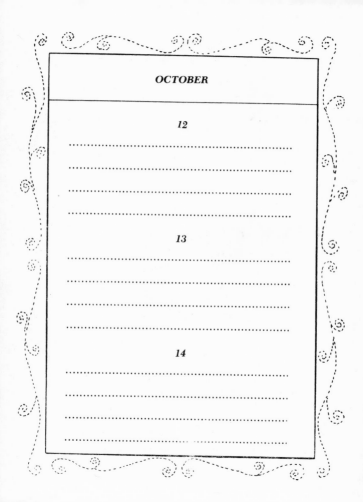

OCTOBER

12

....
....
....
....

13

....
....
....
....

14

....
....
....
....

Use it up, wear it out;
Make it do, or do without.

New England maxim

*Beggar's
Block*

He is richest who is content with least; for contentment is the wealth of nature.

Socrates

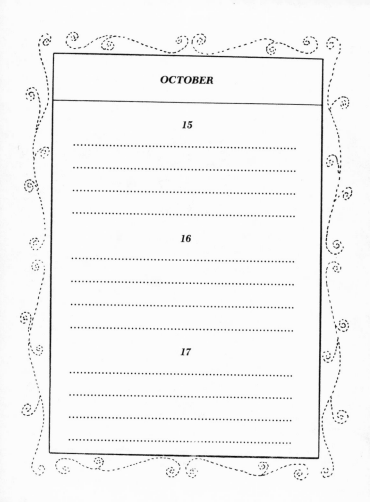

OCTOBER

15

....
....
....
....

16

....
....
....
....

17

....
....
....
....

OCTOBER

*Indian
Trail*

Where we walk to school each day
Indian Children used to play—
All about our native land,
Where the shops and houses stand.

Annette Wynne

Navajo

OCTOBER

18

....
....
....
....

19

....
....
....
....

20

....
....
....
....

OCTOBER

No man is born into the world whose work
Is not born with him; there is always work,
And tools to work withal, for those who will....
James Russell Lowell

*Carpenter's
Square*

It has been said that for a life to be content a
person needs: something to love, something to
do, and something to look forward to.

OCTOBER

21

Cathie Murray 52

.....
.....
.....

22

.....
.....
.....

23

.....
.....
.....
.....

*Captain's
Wheel*

Sunset and evening star,
　And one clear call for me!
And may there be no moaning of the bar,
　When I put out to sea....

Alfred, Lord Tennyson

Compass

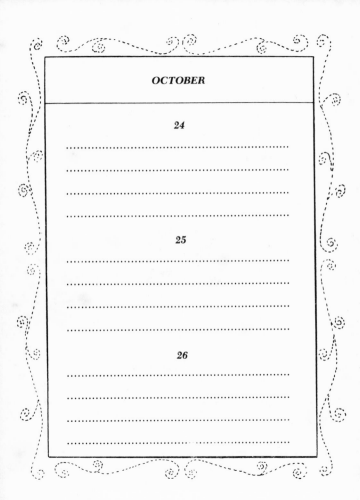

OCTOBER

24

....
....
....
....

25

....
....
....
....

26

....
....
....
....

OCTOBER

Now Israel loved Joseph more than all his children, because he was the son of his old age: and he made him a coat of many colors.

Genesis 37:3

Joseph's Coat

Man's life is laid in the loom of time
 To a pattern he does not see,
While weavers work and shuttles fly
 'Till the dawn of eternity.

Anonymous

OCTOBER

27

....
....
....
....

28

....
....
....
....

29

....
....
....
....

OCTOBER-NOVEMBER

Album Star

...some folks has albums to put folks' pictures in...and some folks has a book and writes down the things that happen...but these quilts is my albums and diaries....I just spread out my quilts ...and it's just like going back fifty or sixty years and living my life over again.

Eliza Calvert Hall

Album Block

OCTOBER-NOVEMBER

30

....
....
....
....

31

....
....
....
....

1

....
....
....
....

NOVEMBER

All sorts of things and weather
Must be taken in together,
To make up a year....

Ralph Waldo Emerson

Weathervane

Life is like a patchwork quilt
And each little patch is a day,
Some patches are rosy, happy and bright,
And some are dark and gray.

Elizabeth Ryan Decoursey

NOVEMBER

Peter Yearly[2]   62

D.D. Barlow[3] III   46

[4]

Whig Rose

Because a woman was not allowed to vote does not mean she was without political convictions. These were often expressed in her quilts, and it is said that more than one Tory husband slept under a Whig Rose quilt.

*54-40
or Fight*

NOVEMBER

5

....
....
....
....

6

....
....
....
....

7

Dan + Ann .... A 81
....
....
....

NOVEMBER

After my boy Razzie died when he was fourteen,
I began to quilt in earnest, all day sometimes....
Seems my mind just couldn't quit planning
patterns and colors, and the piecing, the sewing
with the needle comforted me.

From The Quilters

*Flock
of Geese*

...a rest to [the] mind, a cheerer of [the] spirits,
a diverter of sadness, a calmer of unquiet
thoughts, a moderator of passions, a procurer of
contentedness....

*Sir Henry Wooton (to him a description
of angling—to me, a description of quilting)*

NOVEMBER

8

....
....
....
....

9

Seymour Perkins III 40
....
....
....

10

....
....
....
....

NOVEMBER

*Wild
Waves*

The breaking waves dashed high,
  On a stern and rockbound coast,
And the woods against a stormy sky,
  Their giant branches tossed;
And the heavy night hung dark,
  The hills and waters o'er,
When a band of exiles moored their bark
  On the wild New England shore.
                                    Felicia Hemans

*Ocean
Wave*

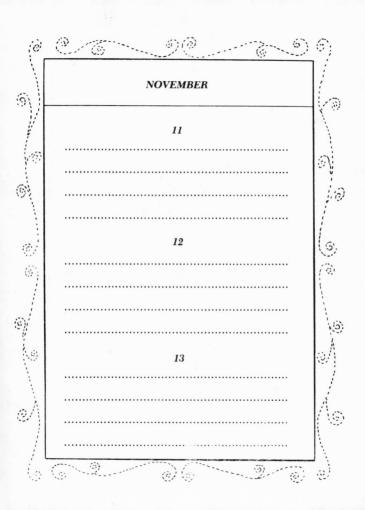

NOVEMBER

11

....
....
....
....

12

....
....
....
....

13

....
....
....
....

*Crosses
and Losses*

And no matter how simple or traditional a pattern, the effect of a quilt is still absolutely original because no two people handle fabric and color the same way.

Beth Gutcheon

*Drunkard's
Path*

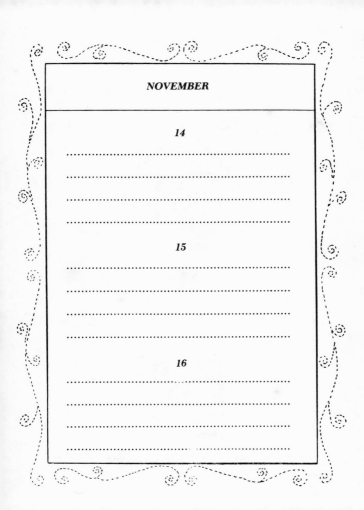

NOVEMBER

14

....
....
....
....

15

....
....
....
....

16

....
....
....
....

NOVEMBER

*Basket
of Scraps*

I liked assorting those little figured bits of cotton cloth, for they were scraps of gowns I had seen worn, and they reminded me of the persons who wore them.

Lucy Larcom

*Shoo
Fly*

NOVEMBER

17

Mary Richards 51

....

....

....

18

....

....

....

....

19

....

....

....

....

NOVEMBER

The dream of a life spent midst peace and plenty, though we think of it as peculiarly American, is a dream as old as the human heart, and one in which all people have shared.

Peace and Plenty

We beseech thee to hear us, Good Lord. That it may please thee to give all nations unity, peace, and concord....and preserve to our use the kindly fruits of the earth so that in due time we may enjoy them....

From The Book of Common Prayer

NOVEMBER

20

....
....
....
....

21

....
....
....
....

22

....
....
....
....

NOVEMBER

*Puss in
the Corner*

Pussy cat, pussy cat, where have you been?
I've been to London to look at the queen.
Pussy cat, pussy cat, what did you there?
I frightened a little mouse under her chair.
                    Old nursery rhyme

Cat and Mice

NOVEMBER

23

Sally Jorgenson 37

....
....
....

24

....
....
....
....

25

....
....
....
....

NOVEMBER

Death was very much a part of our ancestors' lives and like everything else of importance was sewn into their quilts—either in the form of separate blocks or as an entire memory quilt.

Coffin Star

We who now are young and gay
  Like roses in their bloom
Will very soon be old and gray
  And wither in our tomb.

From a sampler, 1837

NOVEMBER

26

....
....
....
....

27

Richard S. Perkins 70

....
....
....

28

....
....
....
....

*Friendship
Dahlia*

Friendship, a dear balm—
Whose coming is as light and music are
'Mid dissonance and gloom....
A solitude, a refuge, a delight.
Percy Bysshe Shelley

*Friendship
Star*

NOVEMBER-DECEMBER

29

....
....
....
....

30

....
....
....
....

1

....
....
....
....

DECEMBER

When the weary day is over
And the world has gone to rest,
When my little bark is dancing o'er the foam,
Like a dove at night returning
To the shelter of her nest,
Seeks my heart again the beacon light of home.
George F. St. Clair

*Beacon
Lights*

But what on earth is half so dear—
So longed for—as the hearth of home?
Emily Bronte

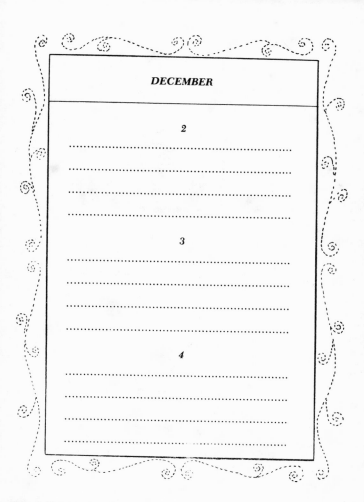

DECEMBER

2

....
....
....
....

3

....
....
....
....

4

....
....
....
....

DECEMBER

Grandmother's Fan

Inanimate objects do gather into themselves something of the character of those who live among them, through association, and this alone makes heirlooms valuable.

Lucy Larcom

Aunt Eliza's Star

DECEMBER

5

....
....
....
....

6

June Barlow 16
....
....
....

7

....
....
....
....

DECEMBER

The beloved Marquis de Lafayette was honored at a banquet in Philadelphia in 1824, during which oranges were served as part of the dessert. He cut the skin of his orange into four parts before peeling it. A young lady asked for the skin as a souvenir, and took it home where it became the inspiration for this patch.

*Lafayette
Orange Peel*

Needlework is the art that tells the truth about the real life of people in their time and place.
Rose Wilder Lane

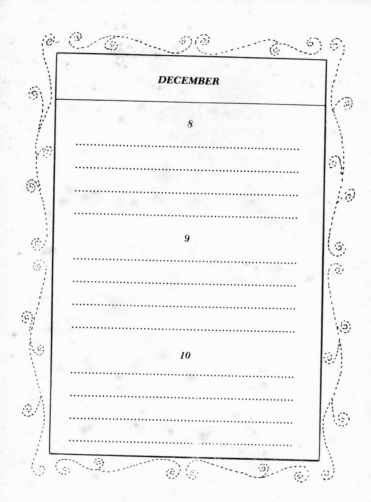

DECEMBER

8

....
....
....
....

9

....
....
....
....

10

....
....
....
....

DECEMBER

*Friendship
Nine Patch*

How much piecing a quilt is like living a life...
you can give the same kind of pieces to two persons, and one will make a "nine patch" and one
will make a "wild goose chase," and there will be
two quilts made out of the same kind of pieces
and just as different as they can be. And that is
just the way with living. The Lord sends us the
pieces, but we can cut them out and put them together pretty much to suit ourselves, and there's
a heap more in the cutting out and the sewing
than there is in the calico.

Eliza Calvert Hall

*Wild
Goose
Chase*

DECEMBER

11

....
....
....
....

12

William R. Peelle III 82
WmK Dunbar 07
Mandy Richards 77
....

13

....
....
....
....

DECEMBER

So many gods, so many creeds,
   So many paths that wind and wind,
   When just the art of being kind
Is all this sad world needs.

Ella Wheeler Wilcox

*Winding
Ways*

No act of kindness, no matter how small, is ever
wasted.

Aesop

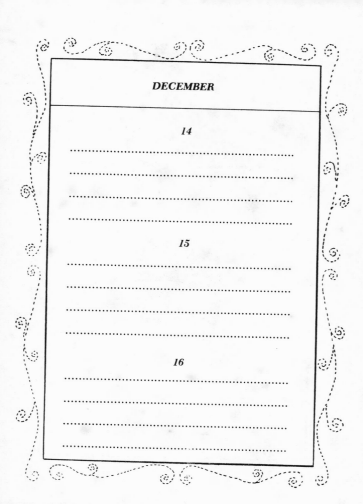

DECEMBER

14

....
....
....
....

15

....
....
....
....

16

....
....
....
....

DECEMBER

In the reign of Edward VI, lands at St. Peter's at Westminister were appropriated to raise money for the repair of St. Paul's in London.

*Robbing
Peter to
Pay Paul*

If I rob Peter to pay Paul
Peter won't be paid at all.

Jeanne Gula

DECEMBER

17

18

Deb Wade

19

Carlton Barlow   16

*Rising
Star*

...and, lo, the star, which they saw in the east, went before them, till it came and stood over where the young child was.

Matthew 2:9

*Star of
Bethlehem*

DECEMBER

20
Elizabeth McGonagle [68]

21
Chuck Jorgenson 36

22

DECEMBER

*Christmas
Tree*

**At Christmas play and make good cheer,
For Christmas comes but once a year.**
Thomas Tusser

*Christmas
Star*

DECEMBER

23

....
....
....
....

24

Jennifer Sonis 7 7
....
....
....

25

....
....
....
....

DECEMBER

In memory's casket
Place one gem for me.
Written in an autograph album, 1893

*Jewels in
a Frame*

Each fragment there is a printed page,
With mem'ries written 'twixt youth and age.
From the song, Patchwork

DECEMBER

26
Timothy   Harrigan 51

....
....
....

27
Benjamin   Jones   86

....
....
....

28

....
....
....
....

DECEMBER

But, at my back I always hear
Time's winged chariot hurrying near;
And yonder all before us lie
Deserts of vast eternity.

Andrew Marvell

*Winged
Square*

The Broken Resolution

Another year departs: the bell is tolled.
—And I intended never to grow old!

Jokun

DECEMBER

29

30

Cinny McGonagle 41
Cheri + Chris 78

31

Jennifer Jorgenson 64

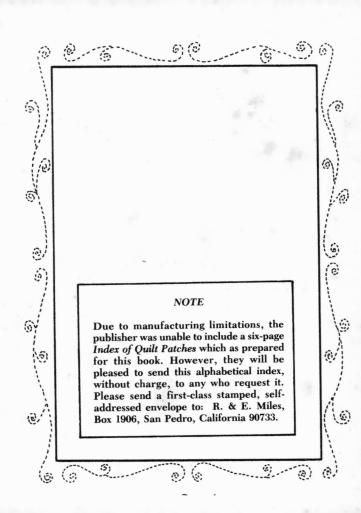

NOTE

Due to manufacturing limitations, the publisher was unable to include a six-page *Index of Quilt Patches* which as prepared for this book. However, they will be pleased to send this alphabetical index, without charge, to any who request it. Please send a first-class stamped, self-addressed envelope to: R. & E. Miles, Box 1906, San Pedro, California 90733.